GW00319909

X IS FOR
UNEXPLAINED

An incredible selection of inexplicable trivia!

LAGOON
BOOKS

Lagoon Books, London

Editor: Heather Dickson
Research: Jenny Lynch, Nick Hoare, Will Young,
David Thompson, Vicky Barber, Helen James
Additional contributors: Jennifer Steele, Rosie Atkins
Page design and layout: Linley Clode
Cover design: Gary Inwood Studios

Published by:
LAGOON BOOKS
PO BOX 311, KT2 5QW, UK

ISBN: 1899712259

© LAGOON BOOKS, 1997
Lagoon Books is a trade mark of Lagoon Trading
Company Limited. All rights reserved.

Printed in Singapore

LAGOON
BOOKS

X

IS FOR
UNEXPLAINED

An incredible selection of inexplicable trivia!

Other titles available from Lagoon Books:

Gift Books

Optical Illusions and Puzzles
ISBN 1899712402

After Dinner Games
ISBN 1899712429

Mind-Bogglers - Bizarre but amazingly true trivia!
ISBN 1899712445

Quiz Books

Where in the World am I? - Mystery Geography Quiz
ISBN 1899712410

Pub Trivia Quiz
ISBN 189971250X

Sports Trivia Quiz
ISBN 1899712267

Who in the World am I? - Mystery Celebrity Quiz
ISBN 1899712275

If you have ever wondered what aliens look like, or why they are fascinated with human beings, then this book is just for you.

Compiled by a dedicated team of supernatural sleuths, especially for all those people curious enough to wonder if we really are alone, it is a totally absorbing read.

Scientific fact or pure science fiction?

Divided into four different sections, X is for UneXplained contains page after page of wildly unbelievable and totally inexplicable trivia questions on UFO sightings, alien abductions, ghostly visitations and other weird and wonderful paranormal phenomena.

Whether read alone, or played as a quiz by a group, you must answer the unanswerable and believe the unbelievable to get the questions right.

Section 1 - UFO Sightings

Twenty multiple choice questions on everything from
flying saucers to evidence of alien activity on earth.

Section 2 - Alien Abductions

Everything from tales of sexual encounters with
beautiful space creatures to claiming compensation
if abducted by aliens, feature in this section.

Section 3 - Paranormal Phenomena

Find out what happened to the fish that fell out
of the sky over India in 1836 and why around 300
people picked the winning number, to become
millionaires, in a Colombian lottery.

Section 4 - Ghostly Visitations

A section of things that go bump -
and much, much more - in the night!

1

UFO
SIGHTINGS

What is the male/
female ratio for
UFO sightings?

a) 23% seen by men: 77%
seen by women

b) 50:50

c) 68% seen by men:
32% by women

The term 'Flying Saucer', is attributed to a remark made by pilot Kenneth Arnold when he saw nine unidentified craft flying in formation over Mount Rainier, Washington State. In his statement he said the craft flew in a bobbing motion...

a) "Like a saucer would if you skipped it across water."

b) "And had a domed shape, like a saucer without its cup."

c) "And shocked me so that my cup and saucer went flying."

What is the means of transport for the famous alien 'Greys'?

a) Cigar-shaped crafts

b) Teleportation

c) Intergalactic motorbikes

4

What is the common link between pre-historic drawings in Val Camonica in Northern Italy, Fergana in Uzbekistan, and Tassili in the Sahara?

a) They all show figures wearing spherical 'astronaut' helmets

b) They all show lizard-like creatures communicating with humans

c) They all show an identical unrecognised combination of stars

A broadsheet published in 1561 in Nuremberg, Germany, describes balls, plates, crosses and tubes of different colours in the sky above the city. What were these UFOs reported to be doing?

a) Dancing in a vertical formation

b) Writing messages in the sky

c) Conducting an aerial battle

On 25 May 1990, three surface-to-air missiles were fired at a giant disc-shaped object 300 metres in diameter hovering above the town of Mary, in Turkmenistan. How did the craft respond?

a) It flashed the Morse code message 'we come in friendship'

b) It destroyed the city

c) It sent out three beams of light which disintegrated the missiles

According to reports of the autopsy carried out on one of the 'alien' pilots of the UFO that crashed at Roswell, New Mexico, in 1947, was the body...?

a) Superficially human, but with unrecognisable internal organs

b) Consistent with that of a four-month-old human foetus that had been subjected to an artificial method of gestation

c) Brightly coloured and glowing

Comet Hale-Bopp has been seen to have a large, mysterious companion. What did the Heaven's Gate cult believe this to be?

a) Aliens preparing to invade the earth

b) A meteorite that will destroy the earth at the Millennium

c) A UFO which would take them to Heaven

W hat 'spaced out' name has been given to Route 375 in the Nevada desert, owing to the incidence of UFO sightings there?

a) The Extraterrestrial Highway

b) Highway to Heaven

c) Starlight Expressway

In 1994, Lt Col Halt reported seeing a UFO in Rendlesham Forest, Suffolk. How did he describe it?

a) He couldn't - he was rendered speechless from the shock

b) "Like a halved melon, only the seeds were like these magnificent lights..."

c) "Red, like the sun coming up in the morning, with a black centre that opened and closed like an eye."

During the reign of Charlemagne, there were many reports of encounters with 'tyrants of the air and their aerial ships'. What action did the Emperor take?

a) He ordered scientists to create flying machines to investigate such phenomena

b) He banned the witnesses from local ale-houses and hostelries

c) He ordered that people reporting such matters be subject to torture and death

Which future
US president
filed a UFO sighting
report in 1957?

a) Jimmy Carter

b) George Bush

c) Ronald Reagan

O ne of the most
famous UFO
encounters occurred
in Sweden in 1958, when
two men encountered
a craft and its four
occupants. What name
did they give to the
beings?

a) 'Greys'
b) 'Lemons'
c) 'Blobs'

In July 1952, repeated UFO sightings sent panic throughout the USAF Air Defense Command. Where were the mysterious lights seen?

a) Hovering over a Frank Sinatra open-air concert in Las Vegas

b) Over the Capitol building in Washington DC

c) Above ICBM silos in Utah

15

What is the average number of witnesses to a UFO sighting?

a) 6.4

b) 2.2

c) 3.1

How was the UFO seen by two men, in a forest in the British Midlands, explained away?

a) As waste gas emissions from a nearby balloon factory

b) As a flying owl, glowing in the dark after eating decaying fungus

c) As a mass hallucination caused by bacteria in a shared pork pie

Who brought traffic to a standstill on the M25 motorway in the UK on 1 April 1989, by decorating a balloon like a spaceship and manning it with a midget dressed as an alien?

a) Noel Edmonds
b) Richard Branson
c) Michael Jackson

Captain Coyne was flying a helicopter to Columbus, Ohio, on 18 October 1973 when he saw a UFO flying straight towards him. What happened next?

a] He was bathed in green light and although he put the chopper into a dive, he ended up at a higher altitude

b] The controls in the cockpit began to melt

c] Neither pilot nor helicopter was ever seen again

What percentage of UFO sightings cannot be explained rationally?

a) 10%

b) 75%

c) 1%

A UFO seen in La Junta, Colorado, in 1975 was compared to which of the following?

a) The Houston Astrodome

b) A doughnut

c) A disco mirrorball

2

ALIEN
ABDUCTIONS

According to Dr Paul Bennewitz, how many people worldwide have actually been abducted and implanted by aliens?

a) 20,000

b) 12

c) 2,000,000

W hich US president is supposed to have set up a permanent committee known as MJ12 (Majority Twelve) to oversee all activities concerned with the alien question?

a) Eisenhower
b) Kennedy
c) Nixon

What happened to frequent abductee Katrina Wilson when she was six years old?

a) She found herself floating along with pod-shaped objects that moved in the same direction as her

b) She disappeared into another dimension at the back of her wardrobe

c) She found that she could read the thoughts of her class-mates

For several months after his alien abduction, what could Soviet aviation mechanic Igor Yadigin not do?

a) Touch planes - if he did, they spontaneously combusted

b) Watch TV - his body distorted the picture if he went near the set

c) Eat strawberries - they brought him out in a rash resembling Egyptian hieroglyphics

What evidence is needed to claim compensation (if insured) for alien abduction?

a] Samples of alien tissue

b] A photograph of the abductee on board the UFO

c] The signature of the abducting alien

What was unusual about Tracy Knapp's abduction experience in 1978?

a] She was in a car which was lifted off the ground and spun through the air

b] She was in a crowd of 10,000 people watching a tennis match between Bjorn Borg and Vitus Geralitus at Wimbledon

c] She wasn't born until January 1979

Where are the most common places for an alien implant to be inserted?

a) The navel or nipple

b) The ear or nose

c) Moles

What part of abductee Barney Hill supposedly fascinated his alien captors?

a) His false teeth

b) His tattoos of his naked wife, Woody Woodpecker and Popeye

c) His leopardskin polyester shorts

In October 1974, Carl Higdon was abducted whilst hunting in Wyoming, USA. What else did the aliens pick up?

a) Five frozen buffalo

b) A beer delivery truck and lots of discarded car wheels

c) A pick-up truck and three lawnmowers

Antonio Villas-Boas claimed to have had sex with a beautiful alien in 1957. How did she respond?

a) She barked like a dog

b) Beams of light came out of her eyes

c) Her head started to hum and vibrate

What happened when frequent abductee Karen Morgan used a video camera to try to prevent abductions?

a) The abductions stopped

b) She captured a shadowy alien face on tape

c) The abductions continued whenever she forgot to turn on the camera

A

According to abductee Herbert Schirmer, what was the purpose of his alien captors' trips to Earth?

a) To kidnap people to use in their 'breeding analysis' programme

b) To correct our imbalance of aggression which has been radiating through the galaxy

c) To terrify, enslave and eventually kill every human being

Charles Hickson was abducted on 11 October 1973 and taken on-board a UFO. What happened next?

a) He was suspended in a room and examined by a free-floating giant eye

b) He was intimately probed by two aliens in masks

c) He found himself on a road in Tijuana, Mexico, with a jelly-like substance on his hands

How did William Spauldings explain the UFO abduction phenomenon in 1982?

a) Angels from Heaven trying to implement God's 'galaxy plan'

b) The testing of mind-control drugs by the CIA

c) Outbreaks of temporary paranoid schizophrenia

When abductee Linda Cortile was dropped back into her bed by aliens how did her husband react?

a) Presuming she had been unfaithful, he shot and wounded her

b) He was rendered speechless for six years

c) He slept through the whole ordeal

Myrna Hansen was abducted in New Mexico on 5 May 1950. What did she see inside the UFO?

a) A statue of a man resembling Glenn Miller

b) Large vats filled with a clear liquid in which human body-parts were floating

c) Models of the White House, the Pentagon, the Kremlin and the Palace of Westminster

After examining UFO abductees, what did electronics expert Dr Paul Bennewitz conclude?

a) That human scientists were working with the aliens to construct a race of hybrids

b) That the human body is built to an alien design

c) That Jesus was a dolphin converted to human form by aliens who have been watching the earth for millions of years

What made aliens believe that abductee Melissa Bucknell was ill?

a) She had thumbs

b) The fact that she needed oxygen to breathe

c) She had dyed part of her black hair blonde

W hat was abducted by aliens from the Watson farm in Mt. Vernon, Missouri?

a) A black cow

b) An entire coop of chickens

c) A 20-year-old cultivator and muckspreader

Travis Walton was abducted in November 1975, whilst trimming trees in Arizona. How did he describe the three aliens who examined him?

a) Like well-developed foetuses, about five feet tall, in tight-fitting, tan-brown robes

b) Like old men with leather faces, but with huge doe-like eyes

c) Like garden gnomes

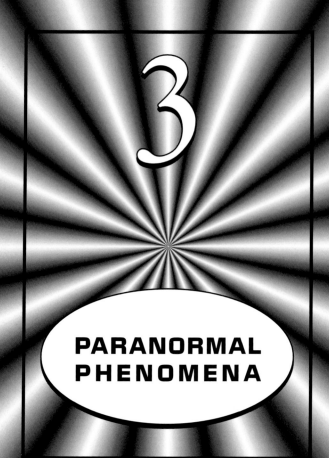

3

PARANORMAL PHENOMENA

What reportedly happens to a 'standing stone' in rural Gloucestershire, England, on Hallowe'en?

a) It rolls around the field it stands in and takes a bite out of an apple if you lay one nearby

b) It turns into a werewolf and terrorises the local community

c) The stone disappears from the field for approximately two hours

The Times reported on 19 April 1836 a fall of fish in Allahabad, India. The fish were dried, and had been out of the water for some time. What happened when they were cooked?

a) They vanished from sight

b) They tasted of venison

c) They turned to blood in the pan

What is remote viewing?

a) Fortune-telling using the patterns of crowd movement seen from a distance

b) The ability to receive TV pictures mentally

c) The ability to see a far away place

The Philadelphia Experiment was a naval experiment in radar invisibility. What mysterious side-effect did it achieve?

a) It created 'ghosts' on radar

b) It made objects vanish completely and irretrievably

c) The teleportation of a battleship over 600km

What did Uri Geller first become famous for?

a) Spoon-bending

b) Eating metal

c) Detecting psychic ability in others

6

N

Naturally vented methane gas 'burps' are used to explain what phenomena?

a) Momentary glimpses of ghostly figures

b) UFO sightings

c) The Bermuda Triangle

H istorical documents detail the bizarre death of the 15th century European knight, Polonus Vorstius. According to contemporary accounts, he ...

a) Spontaneously combusted

b) Was cooked and then eaten by a dragon-like beast

c) Drowned in his armour during a skirmish with a reptilian lake monster

I n 1995, around 300 people used the number '1124' in the Colombian national lottery, winning over £1 million. What had inspired them to pick this number?

a) A fish had recently been caught with the number 1124 inscribed on its side

b) It was the 24th of November

c) A Colombian mystic divined the number correctly in a village newspaper

A cow born in Chaco, Argentina, in 1995 had the same number of testicles as it had legs. How many testicles did it have?

a) Six

b) Four

c) Two

In 1948, Diane Lamb broke two ribs in a train crash. How did her twin sister receive the same injury at the same time?

a) She crashed her car into a tree on an empty road

b) She was thrown from her chair by a stabbing pain

c) She was knocked off her piano stool by her sister's parrot

What did Brian Clements have to do before touching anyone?

a) Wash away the small quantities of highly toxic fungus that his hands, feet and scalp constantly exuded

b) Pray, to prevent bruises (and occasionally wounds) appearing on his hands

c) Discharge the vast quantities of static he generated into an earthed object

In 1982 Ray Barnes witnessed the formation of a crop circle. What accompanied it?

a) A deafening explosion

b) A weird humming noise

c) A thick fog which appeared from nowhere and then disappeared after three minutes

What power was 10-year-old Italian Benedict Supino found to have in 1982?

a) The power to cause dogs to pass out by singing at them

b) The power to set an object on fire by looking at it

c) The power to go into a trance, then recite any of the sayings of Christ in biblical Hebrew, if he adopted a crucifix-like position

What happens to schoolgirl Cloretta Robertson of Oakland, California, every Easter?

a) On Good Friday she goes into a coma until Sunday morning

b) The wounds of Christ on the cross appear on her forehead and hands

c) Wordless songs come non-stop from her mouth for the whole weekend

What happened to Reverend John Henry Lehn in his bathroom in 1921?

a) A snake crawled out of the overflow and joined him in the bath

b) A ghost accompanied him whilst he was sitting on the toilet

c) A ball of lightning came in, rolled around and jumped into the wash basin before disappearing

Who was the famous band leader who vanished on 15 December 1944 carrying an original score of music never before played?

a) Buddy Holly

b) Glenn Miller

c) Busby Berkeley

Why was 'Crocker Land', an island in the Arctic circle, removed from US Hydrographic Office Maps in 1914, only eight years after its discovery in 1906?

a) It sank

b) It was a mirage

c) It erupted and disappeared

In July 1995, a column of migrating toads marched through Liaoning province in northern China. The column stretched for....

a) 1 mile

b) 100 miles

c) 1,000 miles

What amount of water has mysteriously disappeared from various lakes and reservoirs around the world in the last ten years?

a) 3.5 billion gallons exactly from 13 different locations

b) Two million litres

c) Enough to fill the Dead Sea

When Mary Hardy Keeser died in unexplained circumstances in 1951, how was she found?

a) In a heap of ashes with only her liver and a few bones left

b) Looking 20 years younger

c) Doing a handstand

4

GHOSTLY
VISITATIONS

1

What does the Ghost
of Chavanage
House hold in his arms
when he roams the
corridors at night?

a) His head
b) His faithful puppy dog
c) The body of his long-lost
lover

What is a crisis apparition?

a) A ghostly warning prior to disaster

b) The appearance of a ghost at the time of death of a loved one

c) A vision seen in a near-death experience

What is special about Littledean House in England?

a) It is reputed to be the oldest and most haunted house in the country

b) It is visited by aliens every New Year's Day

c) It has a jar made of a stone unknown on this planet

W hat is Camaphouca Castle haunted by?

a] A headless horseman

b] Vampires

c] Poltergeists

5

The Busby Stoop Inn in North Yorkshire had to remove its namesake chair because...

a) It would regularly move by itself, scaring patrons and spilling drinks

b) So many of the people who sat on it died

c) It often appeared to be occupied by a ghostly, hooded figure

The ghosts of the crew of Flight 401 appeared 20 times to passengers....

a) On the same route as the doomed flight

b) On planes repaired with parts from 401

c) On flights with one or more 401 survivors on board

L arry Mead decided to sit all night in a poltergeist-ridden gift shop in Rio Grande, New Jersey, in 1979. What happened to him?

a) He was found choked by two models of the Statue of Liberty

b) He was bombarded with cuddly toys all night

c) He was hit by a fireplace tile

Why did a Taiwanese bus company refuse to make pick-ups from a remote village?

a) Three buses and their drivers had failed to return and no trace of them was ever found

b) Drivers reported a phantom girl passenger who would get on the bus, but was never seen getting off

c) Five different drivers were bitten by snakes on the same stretch of road

In 1987, the Costello family of Apsley in Nottinghamshire, England, were repeatedly sent the message 'A H.' by a poltergeist. How?

a) Bottles of ketchup were knocked over and the sauce moved to form the letters

b) The central heating would send out high-pitched squeals in Morse code

c) A typewriter would constantly type it out

A 12ft incarnation of whom was seen descending from the sky over Fyffe, Alabama, in 1989?

a) Jesus Christ
b) Liberace
c) JFK

On his route from Texas to Florida, what apparition did trucker Hariette Spanabel always see?

a) A Mexican family standing around a burning pick-up truck

b) A truck which would follow him for 30 miles then disappear into thin air

c) A roadside bar full of people, that had disappeared when he returned by day

What did medium Eusapia Palladino manage to do at a séance in 1902?

a) Stop and re-start a volunteer's heart - a previous volunteer went into a coma

b) Levitate three people at once

c) Make six human forms appear, then disappear

E leonore Zugun
complained that
she was the victim of a
poltergeist during 1926.
What evidence did
she have?

a) Symbols written in crayon
would appear on her back

b) Teeth marks and scratches
would regularly flare up on her
arms and face

c) People would hear
mysterious growling noises in
her company

W hat is the trick of the spook at the Tudor Rose Inn, in Fordingbridge, Hampshire, England?

a) He runs his fingers over the hips of the landlady and lady customers

b) He rings the bell

c) He drinks customers' unattended drinks

In January 1982, the New-man family of Sheffield awoke to hear the familiar sound of a poltergeist running through their home, making banging sounds. What was unusual about this night?

a) Percussive Afro-Cuban rhythms were also heard

b) Dark green handprints appeared on the walls, then disappeared

c) The flat was on fire - the poltergeist saved their lives

The commissionaires of which London institution have noticed that if you press the third floor lift button, the lift goes straight up to the sixth floor; but this only happens at night?

a) The Ritz

b) The Palace of Westminster

c) The BBC

Wat sparked off spooks at the Kings Head Pub in Kent, England?

a) The removal of the ancient creaky pub sign

b) The removal of a tombstone from outside the Gents' toilets

c) The removal of a suit of armour propped up at the bar

Where was ghost-hunter Andrew Green asked to investigate ghostly sightings in April 1996?

a) The Royal Albert Hall, London

b) The White House, Washington DC

c) The Winter Palace, St Petersburg

What does poltergeist activity usually centre around?

a) Young girls on the verge of puberty

b) Cemeteries

c) Psychiatric patients

What does the ghost at the Cock and Bottle Inn in Yorkshire, England, do to the female bar staff?

a) Blows kisses

b) Gives a long sexy stare before fading away

c) Pinches their bottoms

Section 1 - UFO Sightings

1 **c)** 68% seen by men: 32% by women

2 **a)** "Like a saucer would if you skipped it across water."

3 **a)** Cigar-shaped crafts

4 **a)** They all show figures wearing spherical 'astronaut' helmets

5 **c)** Conducting an aerial battle

6 **c)** It sent out three beams of light which disintegrated the missiles

7 **b)** Consistent with that of a four-month-old human foetus that had been subjected to an artificial method of gestation

8 **c)** A UFO which would take them to Heaven

9 **a)** The Extraterrestrial Highway

10 **c)** "Red, like the sun coming up in the morning, with a black centre that opened and closed like an eye."

11 **c)** He ordered that people reporting such matters be subject to torture and death

12 **a)** Jimmy Carter

13 **c)** 'Blobs'

14 **b)** Over the Capitol building in Washington DC

15 **b)** 2.2

16 **b)** As a flying owl, glowing in the dark after eating decaying fungus

17 b) Richard Branson

18 a) He was bathed in green light and although he put the chopper into a dive, he ended up at a higher altitude

19 a) 10%

20 b) A doughnut

Section 2 - Alien Abductions

1 c) 2,000,000

2 a) Eisenhower

3 a) She found herself floating along with pod-shaped objects that moved in the same direction as her

4 b) Watch TV - his body distorted the picture if he went near the set

5 c) The signature of the abducting alien

6 a) She was in a car which was lifted off the ground and spun through the air

7 b) The ear or nose

8 a) His false teeth

9 a) Five frozen buffalo

10 a) She barked like a dog

11 c) The abductions continued whenever she forgot to turn on the camera

12 a) To kidnap people to use in their 'breeding analysis' programme

13 a) He was suspended in a room and examined by a free-floating giant eye

14 b) The testing of mind-control drugs by the CIA

15 c) He slept through the whole ordeal

16 b) Large vats filled with a clear liquid in which human body-parts were floating

17 a) That human scientists were working with the aliens to construct a race of hybrids

18 c) She had dyed part of her black hair blonde

19 a) A black cow

20 a) Like well-developed foetuses, about five feet tall, in tight-fitting, tan-brown robes

Section 3 - Paranormal Phenomena

1 a) It rolls around the field it stands in and takes a bite out of an apple if you lay one nearby

2 c) They all turned to blood in the pan

3 c) The ability to see a place far away

4 c) The teleportation of a battleship over 600km

5 a) Spoon-bending

6 c) The Bermuda Triangle

7 a) Spontaneously combusted

8 a) A fish had recently been caught with the number 1124 inscribed on its side

9 a) Six

10 b) She was thrown from her chair by a stabbing pain

11 c) Discharge the vast quantities of static he generated into an earthed object

12	b)	A weird humming noise
13	b)	The power to set an object on fire by looking at it
14	b)	The wounds of Christ on the cross appear on her forehead and hands
15	c)	A ball of lightning came in, rolled around and jumped into the wash basin before disappearing
16	b)	Glenn Miller
17	b)	It was a mirage
18	c)	1,000 miles
19	a)	3.5 billion gallons exactly from 13 different locations
20	a)	In a heap of ashes with only her liver and a few bones left

Section 4 - Ghostly Visitations

1	a)	His head
2	b)	The appearance of a ghost at the time of death of a loved one
3	a)	It is reputed to be the oldest and most haunted house in the country
4	b)	Vampires
5	b)	So many of the people who sat on it died
6	b)	On planes repaired with parts from 401

7	c)	He was hit by a fireplace tile
8	b)	Drivers reported a phantom girl passenger who would get on the bus, but was never seen getting off
9	c)	A typewriter would constantly type it out
10	b)	Liberace
11	b)	A truck which would follow him for 30 miles then disappear into thin air
12	c)	Make six human forms appear, then disappear
13	b)	Teeth marks and scratches would regularly flare up on her arms and face
14	a)	He runs his fingers over the hips of the landlady and lady customers
15	c)	The flat was on fire - the poltergeist saved their lives
16	c)	The BBC
17	b)	The removal of a tombstone from outside the Gents' toilets
18	a)	The Royal Albert Hall, London
19	a)	Young girls on the verge of puberty
20	b)	Gives a long, sexy stare before fading away

If you enjoyed this book,

you will love X is for UneXplained,

a board game of the paranormal,

alien life, UFOs and the unexplained!

Suitable for 2-5 players,

X is for UneXplained - The Game,

is available from all good gift shops

or by mail order from

Lagoon Games, PO Box 311, KT2 5QW, UK.